LOVE IS BLUE

HLE

HAL LEONARD EUROPE
DISTRIBUTED BY MUSIC SALES

EXCLUSIVE DISTRIBUTORS
MUSIC SALES LIMITED
8/9 FRITH STREET, LONDON W1V 5TZ, ENGLAND
MUSIC SALES PTY LIMITED
120 ROTHSCHILD AVENUE, ROSEBERY,
NSW 2018, AUSTRALIA.

ORDER NO. HLE90000022
ISBN 0-7119-6304-5

COVER DESIGN BY STUDIO TWENTY, LONDON
PRINTED IN THE UNITED STATES OF AMERICA

YOUR GUARANTEE OF QUALITY...
AS PUBLISHERS, WE STRIVE TO PRODUCE EVERY BOOK
TO THE HIGHEST COMMERCIAL STANDARDS.
THIS BOOK HAS BEEN CAREFULLY DESIGNED TO
MINIMISE AWKWARD PAGE TURNS AND TO MAKE
PLAYING FROM IT A REAL PLEASURE. THROUGHOUT,
THE PRINTING AND BINDING HAVE BEEN PLANNED TO
ENSURE A STURDY, ATTRACTIVE PUBLICATION WHICH
SHOULD GIVE YEARS OF ENJOYMENT. IF YOUR COPY
FAILS TO MEET OUR HIGH STANDARDS, PLEASE INFORM
US AND WE WILL GLADLY REPLACE IT.

MUSIC SALES' COMPLETE CATALOGUE DESCRIBES
THOUSANDS OF TITLES AND IS AVAILABLE IN FULL
COLOUR SECTIONS BY SUBJECT, DIRECT FROM MUSIC
SALES LIMITED. PLEASE STATE YOUR AREAS OF
INTEREST AND SEND A CHEQUE/POSTAL ORDER FOR
£1.50 FOR POSTAGE TO:
MUSIC SALES LIMITED, NEWMARKET ROAD,
BURY ST. EDMUNDS, SUFFOLK IP33 3YB, ENGLAND.

VISIT THE INTERNET MUSIC SHOP
http://www.musicsales.co.uk

ANGEL EYES

Words by EARL BRENT
Music by MATT DENNIS

AUTUMN LEAVES
(Les Feuilles Mortes)

English lyric by JOHNNY MERCER
French lyric by JACQUES PREVERT
Music by JOSEPH KOSMA

Slowly, with much feeling

gold. I see your lips, _____ the sum-mer kiss - es, _____ the sun-burned
mais. Nous vi-vions tous, _____ Les deux en - sem - ble, _____ Toi qui m'ai-

hands _____ I used to hold. Since you went a - way _ the days grow long, _____ and soon I'll
mais _____ Moi qui t'ai mais. Mais la vie sé-pare Ceux qui s'ai - ment _____ Tout dou - ce-

hear _____ old win - ter's song. But I miss you most of all my
ment _____ Sans faire de bruit. Et la mer ef - fa - ce sur le

dar - ling, when au - tumn leaves start to fall. The fall - ing fall.
sa - ble Les pas des a - mants dé - su - nis. C'est une chan - nis.

BLACK COFFEE

Words and Music by PAUL FRANCIS WEBSTER
and SONNY BURKE

DON'T EXPLAIN

Words and Music by BILLIE HOLIDAY
and ARTHUR HERZOG

CAN'T HELP LOVIN' DAT MAN
from SHOW BOAT

Words by OSCAR HAMMERSTEIN
Music by JEROME KERN

CRAZY

Words and Music by
WILLIE NELSON

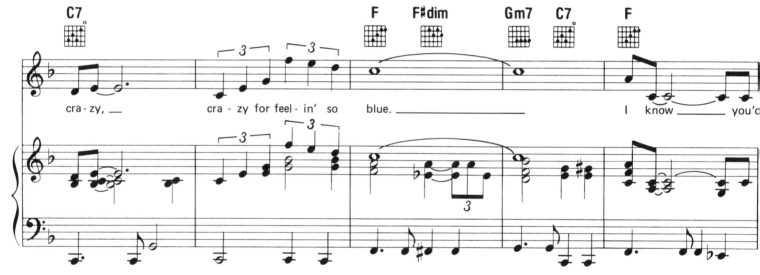

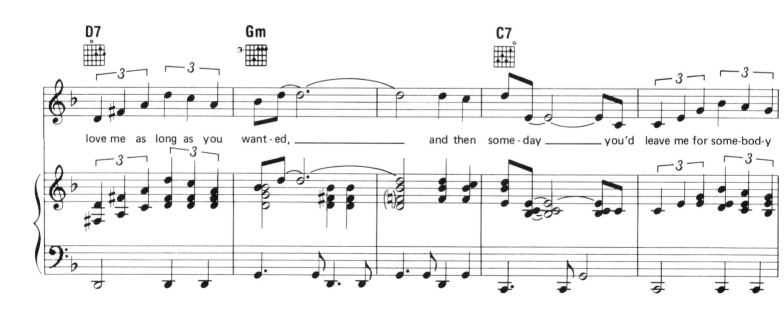

THE END OF A LOVE AFFAIR

Words and Music by
EDWARD C. REDDING

FALLING IN LOVE AGAIN
(Can't Help It)
from the Paramount Picture THE BLUE ANGEL

Words and Music by
FREDERICK HOLLANDER

GOOD MORNING HEARTACHE

Words and Music by DAN FISHE
IRENE HIGGINBOTHAM and ERVIN DRA

HERE'S THAT RAINY DAY
from CARNIVAL IN FLANDERS

Words and Music by JOHNNY BURKE
and JAMES VAN HEUSEN

I GOT IT BAD AND THAT AIN'T GOOD

Words by PAUL FRANCIS WEBSTER
Music by DUKE ELLINGTON

40

I SHOULD CARE

Words and Music by SAMMY CAHN,
AXEL STORDAHL and PAUL WESTON

I WILL WAIT FOR YOU
from THE UMBRELLAS OF CHERBOURG

Music by MICHEL LEGRAN
Original French Text by JACQUES DEM
English Lyrics by NORMAN GIMBE

I'LL BE AROUND

Words and Music by
ALEC WILDER

I'LL NEVER SMILE AGAIN

Words and Music by
RUTH LOWE

MCA music publishing

IN A SENTIMENTAL MOOD

Words and Music by DUKE ELLINGTON,
IRVING MILLS and MANNY KURTZ

I'M SORRY

Words and Music by RONNIE SEL
and DUB ALBRITTE

MCA music publishing

IT MUST BE HIM

Words and Music by GILBERT BECAUD and MAURICE VIDALI
English Adaptation by MACK DAVI

JUST ONE MORE CHANCE

Words by SAM COSLOW
Music by ARTHUR JOHNSTON

JUST FOR A THRILL

Words and Music by LIL ARMSTRONG
and DON RAY

LOVE, LOOK AWAY
from FLOWER DRUM SONG

Words by OSCAR HAMMERSTEIN
Music by RICHARD RODGERS

LOVER MAN
(Oh, Where Can You Be?)

by JIMMY DAVIS, ROGER "RAM" RAMIRE
and JIMMY SHERMA'

LUSH LIFE

Words and Music by
BILLY STRAYHORN

THE MAN THAT GOT AWAY
from the Motion Picture A STAR IS BORN

Music by HAROLD ARLEN
Lyric by IRA GERSHWIN

Slowly, but insistently

MORE THAN YOU KNOW

Words by WILLIAM ROSE and EDWARD ELISCU
Music by VINCENT YOUMANS

Slowly, With Expression

NOBODY KNOWS YOU WHEN YOU'RE DOWN AND OUT

Key of F (C-E)

Tune Uke
G C E A

Words and Music by
JIMMIE COX

Symbols for Guitar, Diagrams for Ukulele.

SMOKE GETS IN YOUR EYES
from ROBERTA

Words by OTTO HARBACH
Music by JEROME KERN

SOLITUDE

Words and Music by DUKE ELLINGTON,
EDDIE De LANGE and IRVING MILLS

Slowly, with expression

In my sol - i - tude _____ you haunt

me _____ with re - ver - ies _____ of days gone

by. _____ In my sol - i - tude _____

THE VERY THOUGHT OF YOU

Words and Music by
RAY NOBLE

TELL ME ON A SUNDAY

from SONG & DANCE

Music by ANDREW LLOYD WEBBER
Lyrics by DON BLACK

Don't write a let-ter when you want to leave. Don't call me at three A. M. from a friend's a-part-ment, I'd like to choose how I

Let me down ea-sy, no big song and dance. No long fa-ces, no long looks, no deep con-ver-sa-tion, I know the way we should

THANKS FOR THE MEMORY

from the Paramount Picture BIG BROADCAST OF 1938

Words and Music by LEO ROB
and RALPH RAING

THESE FOOLISH THINGS
(Remind Me of You)

Words by HOLT MARVEL
Music by JACK STRACHEY and HARRY LIN

WHEN SUNNY GETS BLUE

Lyric by JACK SEG
Music by MARVIN FISH

WHEN THE SUN COMES OUT

Lyrics by TED KOEHLER
Music by HAROLD ARLEN

WHY WAS I BORN?

from SWEET ADELINE

Words by OSCAR HAMMERSTEIN
Music by JEROME KERN

WOMAN ALONE WITH THE BLUES

Words and Music by
WILLARD ROBISON

YESTERDAYS
from ROBERTA

Words by OTTO HARBA[...]
Music by JEROME KE[...]

YOU DON'T KNOW WHAT LOVE IS

Words and Music by DON RA
and GENE DePA

Lyrics:
You don't know __ what love is __ un-til you've learned the mean-ing __ of the blues, un-til you've loved a love you've had to

YOU DON'T BRING ME flowers

Words by NEIL DIAMON
MARILYN BERGMAN and ALAN BERGM
Music by NEIL DIAMO

Slowly and freely

You don't bring me flow - ers; you don't sing me love songs.

You hard - ly talk to me an - y-more when you come through the door at the end of the day.

I re - mem-ber when you could-n't wait to love me,